THE STAR
OF BETHLEHEM

A SCIENTIFIC EXPLANATION –
THE REAL STORY

*The significance of the star of Bethlehem in the true
relationship between man, God and science*

Alan Powell

Published by Dr. Alan L.T. Powell,
10 Elm Rd, Stowmarket, IP14 1QW, England.

Printed by Polstead Press,
5a The Maltings, Stowupland Road,
Stowmarket, IP14 5AG

"Let everyone in the world fear the Lord,
and let everyone stand in awe of Him.
For when He spoke, the world began.
It appeared at His command"

Psalm 33, v 8 and 9

CONTENTS

ABOUT THE AUTHOR

Alan L. T. Powell, PhD in astrophysics, M.Sc in Mathematics (London), M.Sc in astronomy (Sussex), B.Sc (London) in mathematics, B.Sc in Physics (Exeter), PGCE (Sussex), ICTC in counselling (Oxford) and FRAS is well qualified to speak out on this subject. He is internationally recognised for his work in such diverse subjects as Astrophysics, microwave technology, plasma physics and super-sonic dynamics. He has over 30 published scientific papers to his credit. Outside work he has interests in Evangelism, Counselling, Boys Brigade, Bridge, Rambling, Tennis, Advanced Driving and Voluntary work.

PREFACE

My original intention when planning this booklet was to demonstrate that previous attempts at explaining the nature of the Star of Bethlehem were flawed. This astronomical object is only described in the Holy Bible, namely Matthew chapter 2, and crucially some elements of its nature were overlooked or ignored in an attempt to find a satisfactory explanation of the event. The obvious solution that it was a miraculous event, heralding the arrival of a man with unique powers, called Jesus, who performed well-documented miracles, was dismissed as a non-scientific solution. Why these events only have been selected from the Bible for special treatment by scientists and in particular astronomers is one of conjecture. Perhaps they are wed to the hypothesis that everything can be explained by science.

There are many other miraculous events described in the Holy Bible, such as creation, the great flood involving Noah's ark, Moses and the burning bush, the virgin birth of Jesus, the resurrection of Jesus, to name just a few. Amongst these, none has been considered in any depth, except for the creation of the universe.

Alarmingly an increasingly number of Christians accept 'The Big Bang' as the start of an evolutionary process that brings us today's cosmos and our world on this planet earth. Other miraculous events are usually dismissed as myths or not worthy of investigation. Charles Darwin, considered to be the father of the theory of evolution was forced into publication when he realised that he could be out-gunned by one of his rivals who had come to the same conclusion. This was the start of the notion that the publication of scientific papers was an instrument to gain credibility amongst one's fellow scientists, which today has reached alarming proportions. Daily we hear of new research into some obscure subject in the news by radio, television or in popular papers. We never hear the credentials of the author or little about the assumptions made in coming to the particular conclusion.

Many scientists who are Christians believe the God of the Bible and do not believe the theory of evolution but keep quiet for fear of being ridiculed. This is a type of persecution which is mild compared with some physical and mental persecution that Christian experience in other parts of the world. Other scientists admit that science has not all the answers and points to an unknown force outside nature. Among these are well known scientists Einstein, Stephen Hawkins and Sir Martin Rees (the present Astronomer Royal). The acceptance of the theory of evolution involves a great step of faith into the unknown based on unfounded assumptions, which are made on little evidence for a connection between a vast array of disconnected and undocumented observations.

At the present time there is no understanding why two masses attract one another, why charged particles of the same type of charge repel one another or why charged particles of the same charge stick together in the nucleus of an atom. These properties are fundamental to the theory of evolution of the universe. There is a large number of assumed discontinuities or jumps in the smooth evolutionary path from atoms to man. Atomic constants and the speed of light are considered, without any evidence for this being so, to be constant throughout time. Many concepts like the Theory of Relativity or the nature of the quasars have to be modified from the simple initial concept to take into account new observations.

My understanding of who God is and how He created the world is still a mystery to me. However, it is much easier to believe in God than 'science has all the answers therefore there is no God'. It is very hard to believe that out of random chaos can come a world of

9

wonder, order and with definite species of fauna and flora. My knowledge of God has been through the written world of the Bible and my personal spiritual connection through prayer and experiencing of the presence of God through my heart and mind. This gives me to wonder what God thinks of our paltry attempts to understand how the cosmos came about. Mankind finds it hard to grasp the notion that time and space has been created for us to develop in. His thinking is not our thinking. All this has led to me, slowly and faltering, as finding ones way through a wood, for the last seventy plus years, to the present strap line on my T-shirt – 'There positively is a God so stop worrying and enjoy life'. This is a reaction to the 2009 campaign slogan on the London buses 'probably there is not a God'!

In this work it is my intention to demonstrate that in this simple concept of the Star of Bethlehem scientists have ignored the obvious solution that it is a miraculous event that can be explained within the bounds of physics. Instead they have omitted important aspects of its well-documented features to come up with in some cases, obtuse solutions. On the other side of the coin a Christian scientist, Dr Denis Alexander, in his recent book entitled 'Creation or Evolution – Do we have to choose', takes another viewpoint. In the reference to the creation account in the Bible he considers these words to be figurative. He states that he has never met a Christian who does not take the early Chapters of the Bible figuratively. He then goes on to suggest that Christians who bat on the side of biblical creation should use all their resources for evangelism. This poses the question why is he using his time, energy and finances writing his book, giving talks and having book signings instead of evangelising the Word of God. Making such incomprehensible statements does nothing to draw me to his conclusion, in fact just the reverse. He does not reach those of a simple faith who believe that the Bible is the inspired word of God, and that He created the earth in six days. In creation of the cosmos and in particular our world there is an in-built history. If Adam, instead of letting Eve pick the apples, had chopped down the tree, he would have seen rings of growth giving the tree a history. The same could be said for all the other features of our known world and cosmos. They have been created with a history.

DEDICATION

This booklet is dedicated to the memory of my only son, the much loved Christopher Powell, who died of cancer in 2002. He was a 'chip off the old block' and is sadly missed by family, friends and work colleagues.

ACKNOWLEDGEMENTS

My parents allowed my sister and I to develop from birth to teenager without restriction. This has made me sure of my own opinion, but at the same time willing to listen. In my middle age I recognize the part played by Tom Rudge, Peter Hattingh, Jack Munting and others from the Pretoria Brethren Assembly in helping me to cross the line from being an atheist to becoming a Christian. They were very patient with me when I questioned their belief. Especially when questioning the hard sayings of Jesus. Steve Bishop, Adriana Peacock, Richard Weaver and Don Egan for helping me to get this into print. Without question this booklet would not have happened without the help and encouragement of my fellow Christians, mentors and friends of over twenty years. Recently my long discussion, by email with John Mundy, has made me see how strong my faith has become whilst he argued the case for atheism with me.

This booklet was produced, against all the odds, in an unconducive atmosphere for serious work or study at the local Stowmarket library. This, one of the worst children's internet style cafés, in which silence is not golden but decidedly muddy. In all this chaos most of the staff cannot be more helpful and friendly. Mr R. McMaster, Head of Services Development at Suffolk County Council told me that he is happy with the service provided at the Suffolk Library.

The author is responsible for any mistakes, errors and insults. None are intended and the author apoligises unreservedly. There is only one man who did not make mistakes – and his name was Jesus, who has been my best friend and inspiration for just over 35 years. Without him none of this would be possible.

INTRODUCTION

The purpose of this booklet is to explain the nature of the Star of Bethlehem. There have been many books, scientific papers, TV programmes and lectures on the subject, which have attempted to explain the nature of this 'star' in terms of known astronomical objects or physical phenomenon. When due consideration is given to the properties of this object, based on the account only given in the Bible, the observations, made by the wise men on a protracted journey, do not fit previous explanations of the nature of the 'star'.

My previous attempts to get my research published in scientific papers or a brief account into various daily papers from the Daily Mail upward have failed. All this has met with a stony silence. Perhaps this was due to a lack of interest in the subject or an objection to the findings. There have been countless articles written by various authors ranging from popular books by Sir Patrick Moore to serious scientific research papers. All of these either come to a conclusion omitting some of the salient points of the account in the Bible, or, as in Sir Patrick Moore's latest book, stating there is no known object fitting the bill. My reason for writing this booklet is in the hope that it will make some worthwhile contribution to knowledge. Also encourage thoughts as to why we are here on earth and to introduce the notion that not all phenomena can be explained by science. This is my personal swansong in life. Although my life has been enjoyable and varied in a quest for knowledge and the understanding of life, I am aware that my contribution in science has been minimal, however this has not dampened my enthusiasm for scientific research.

To the man in the street much of science today is concerned with complicated scenarios that need a great deal of background knowledge to make them comprehensible. Most of my scientific research has fallen into the annals of dusty books and scientific papers lost in the 'mist of time'. At one time the 'googling' of my full name would bring up a sales item in Amazon of the last of the research paper for the Royal Greenwich Observatory. Amazon have either sold out or more likely they have binned the remaining copies due to lack of interest. While this particular paper should be singled out for mention is rather bizarre. Entitled 'van der Held curves of growth' it has been linked with the growth of embryos! Not a subject encountered in astrophysics.

The object of the booklet is to explain in simple terms, avoiding any serious or complicated mathematical equations, the nature of this object in the sky that caught the notice of some wise men in Asia, who set out on a two year journey around 0 AD to find the Messiah. One could ask oneself what has science done for mankind? The advancement in medical procedures, electronic devices, computers etc during my lifetime has been mind blowing even to me as a scientist. However, we now have microscopes that can form an image of the individual atoms that can be displayed on a screen. We have telescopes that can see to the very faint objects in the sky. The Large Hydron accelerator of atomic particles will soon be working and it commands a disproportionate amount of media interest. This will look for the so-called God particle. The cement that holds atoms together against the repulsive forces of protons. The telescope in space can see further detail than the terrestrial variety. There is the capability of putting man onto planets in our Solar system. This is all done in the quest for knowledge, and to demonstrate the ingenuity of mankind. Science started out to be a fairly simple exercise for man's mind into the observable nature of life, using understandable concepts. Research however usually involves a great amount of money, teams of men and years of detailed study. Surely this money would be better spent on solving the problem of feeding and healing the poor of the world?

Scientists can go on peeling the successive layers of the 'onion of knowledge' only to find another layer. Each layer bringing with it another set of more complicated observations to be explained in terms of a cogent theory, usually at the expense of the previously well accepted explanation.

Even the once cherished Theory of Relativity has been found wanting. The theory of stellar evolution proposes the so-called 'dark matter' accounts for the observed universe. All this depends on fundamental, and in some cases rather fairy tale assumptions. Ted Jaeckel in his book entitled 'The God Particle' proposes another, yet untested, particle to explain how the fundamental characteristics of matter are explained. He goes against the conventional approach to the problem of finding a fundamental particle. This has some rather unusual properties to explain how the physics of nature functions. However, this does not explain why two masses attract or even why they do not repel. It brings in another level of complication.

In an effort to find cheap sources of energy, experiments are being conducted to harness the source of energy of the Sun. This has involved fifty years of research using increasingly bigger machines at huge expense in time and of money. One wonders if this is just a 'big boy's toy' or it has a real chance of producing usable energy. The energy will finally be produced in the form of extremely high energy neutrons. The energy from these can only be harnessed by causing them to react with a large mass of lithium. Some neutrons will escape and react with the containers and surrounding matter that will then become radioactive.

Promoting the theory of evolution is another branch of science that, in Darwin's bicentenary year, is another example of science for science's sake. David Attenborough bandies on about ages of animals existence on earth as if it had been proven beyond doubt. Whereas in fact one could drive a carriage and horses through the theory. Apparently the proposition of the survival of the fittest has already been abandoned. Any evolution from one species to another to make the so-called 'tree of life' now has to be accredited to mutation. However, there have been no fossils found that show this transition from one well defined species to another. Any similarity in the bone structure, embryo or DNA of species can just as easily be accredited to a single creator. In the case of mutation in humans, the abnormalities do not enhance or improve the quality of the offspring. The natural evolution of man has been an increase in brain size due to increased use. There has not been any signs of a radical jump to a new species.

This type of misrepresentation does nothing to promote the concept of complete infallibility of science to explain to the world in which we live. This is demonstrated nowhere more than in the scientific explanation of the Star of Bethlehem as will be shown in the last chapter of this booklet. Science in some areas has served us well. Though it is argueable whether some of the outcome has improved our standard of living. Certainly in the western world, life can be stressful for those trying to get ahead of 'the pack' in an ever increasingly more technical world. The advent of computers has not, as promised, made life easier instead it is more frantic. Our life has been made easier with the range of white appliances. The wealth of knowledge, sometimes of dubious origin and worth, opened up to us via the internet, is mind blowing.

The advances in medicines and living conditions have extended our life expectancy in the richer parts of the world. All this comes at the expense of quality of life and the burden of stress. Whilst the third world is languishing in poverty and sickness, advanced medical techniques are used on treating pets in the 'first world'.

Before the question of the true nature of the 'Star of Bethlehem' can be presented, the writer's background and credentials need to be established to make the arguments credible. This is done in Chapter 1 for the scientific background and in chapter 2 for the Christian experience.

Chapter 1

BECOMING A SCIENTIST

I was born in Ilford, Essex in 1933 and my father was an industrial chemist. I too from an early age had a longing to become a scientist. As a very young boy my inquisitive mind would make me test to see if the notice 'wet paint' was really true. Sometimes with dire consequences. My father used to tell me that a car used no petrol when idling. It took me sometime to realise my father meant little petrol. My mind has always questioned statements and dealt with the detail of explanation. I had hoped to make some mind blowing discovery or at least make a significant contribution to the world's knowledge, an invention or to make the world a better place to live in. To my chagrin these objectives were not to be achieved in any significant way. Hence the reason for writing about The Star of Bethlehem is the hope of making some mark in the thirst for knowledge.

At the outbreak of war my father was employed by the mining firm Rio Tinto at Stratford in London. This was a German owned firm and was therefore closed. My father became unemployed. Eventually he found a job and was transferred to Cardiff in Wales. Before going to Wales our family spent three months in Coventry which turned out to be more dangerous than living in Ilford due to the bombing of the munitions factory. Cardiff was a great place to develop as a child. The school was close to an American Army camp, which gave us a different culture to absorb. Also my first experience of school was standing up to sing the national anthem. Instead of God save the King, it was Mae hen wlad Fy Nnadau (Land of my fathers).

My education continued at the Wanstead County High School on return to Ilford after WW2. The choice was down to my mother, who thought the uniform was better than the local Ilford County High School for Boys! This was a co-educational grammar school, which was quite a rarity in 1945. As my education was transferred from Cardiff Grammar School my placement was in the lower stream of the second year. As a result of the end of first year's examinations, my place was still in the lower stream. A new headmaster, with radical ideas on the education of lower stream pupils, was then appointed after my first year, which affected my education in three ways. Instead of the usual demise of the lower stream having the worst teachers, our form had the best. Also for non-academic subjects, the boys joined the top stream boys. The general certificate of education examination would be taken three months later in December 1949. This social aspect of being with brighter pupils meant that our class behaviour improved. At primary school in Wales mental arithmetic had come easy to me and I suddenly found mathematics to be my best subject and found it comparatively easy. English and specially English Literature was another story. Also my position in the form at the end of term results was in the first two places. This provided me with an incentive to work harder and keep the top position. This transformed my work ethic from being the forms joker, a characteristic still retained today, to becoming a more rounded person with a good work ethic. My nickname was "Prof", coined by my former teacher Mr Gibbons.

Shortly before the general schools certificate, I surprised my closest friend, who was also a classmate, by telling him that play was not on the agenda as revision had taken preference. This surprised him, as my reputation of being the joker of the class did not warrant such a reply. Matriculation was my reward for hard work, seeing the results pinned on the school door by torch light one dark evening in January 1950. This was a surprise to me and even more so to my classmates. Later, a further surprise was my discovery that my physics marks were the highest (96%) in the history of the school. My sister was already at Hull university college studying languages and it came apparent that the possibility of a place in university was open to me. This created a problem in the school educational policy as three months of the sixth form studies had been missed by my delayed taking of the general certificate of education. Scholars from my class were not expected to continue in the sixth form. So this delay was factored out of the study timetable for future generations of students.

In the sixth form my studies were in Physics, Chemistry, Pure and Applied Mathematics. These continued and ended in my obtaining an Open Scholarship in Physics to Exeter University College and a State Scholarship. These would provide me with all my tuition fees, board and lodging, and remarkably a little pocket money, which was really meant for my parents to provide for me in the vacations. How times have changed! At the time it seemed unfair to me that we had this grant and the promise of a well paid job. The paying back of the fees would have been acceptable to me. The Government could only do this when 2% of school leavers went to University. Now everybody has been so better educated or the examinations have been dumbed down so that nearer 50% attend. There is nothing I have seen of the education system to suggest the former is not preferable.

In 1955 my reward for three years of pleasure and

hard work was a disappointing second class Special Physics degree granted by Exeter University for the first time. Previously Exeter College took External London University examinations. The notification of the change of syllabus, from London University to that of the newly formed Exeter University came as a complete surprise. This meant that parts of the old syllabus were no longer needed. However, some of the lectures that had been ignored by me as they were not on the London University syllabus, were now needed and could not be covered in time for examinations. Consequently this ruined my, and other students, chances of obtaining a first class degree. Another disappointment in my life.

My father, who was close to final retirement at 69 years of age, was anxious to see me settled in a job. So the invitation for me to undertake research in Physics at the University was declined; another error of judgement. My choice was either two years of National Service or four years doing scientific research for defence. The latter was my choice – another bad 'call'. My offers were from the Bristol Aeroplane Company, who would not tell me what the work was to be undertaken, or where the work was to take place and the Atomic Weapons Research Establishment at Foulness, who were more forthcoming as to the work to be undertaken. As the former demanded a knife, fork and spoon for their canteen, the latter was my choice!

That small factor meant that my life would take a quite different course. How it would differ would be hard to imagine. One hopes that my choice of path was the superior one. At least it has been an interesting one.

For the first four years at Foulness my work centred around the innovation of new methods of tracking the flight of metal plates driven by high explosives. These move at supersonic speeds and destroy everything in their path. This involved me in the world of electronics and microwaves. These were happy times when my scientific assistant became my wife and were later graced by two delightful children, both high-spirited. My experience included spending three months in the Australian Nullarbor Plain at Maralinga as part of the diagnostic team for the atomic bomb trials in 1957. Health and Safety was not an issue when three of us headed down on Safari with a Land Rover and a trailer full of jerry cans of petrol and three mattresses strapped on top. We had no map, no compass, no first aid training or equipment and no mobile. On reflection this was foolhardy to say the least. How we were given permission is a mystery. We followed a sheep track which crossed the main east west railway and highway. Ignorant of any deadly animal life we threw three mattresses on the ground and covered ourselves with blankets and went to sleep in open ground. We awoke soaked with morning dew. At the head of the Bight we encountered an albatross who refused to fly and a hot air blowhole. It was a great time and the beginning of life's adventure.

In 1960 my work moved, at my request, to research into high energy electro-magnetic shock waves. These produced temperatures in excess of a million degrees in a small chamber 2cm x 2cm x 8cm by discharging a large current from low inductance condensers in a short space of time. With the full support of the AWRE my qualifications were enhanced by obtaining a BSc and MSc with distinction in Mathematics part time at Chelsea College London. This work on high speed shock waves had significance in the production of energy from a fusion reactor and the ZETA machine at Harwell.

Now with x billion of pounds, where x is a large number, the work is progressing at Culham, England and elsewhere. Even if the concept is made to work, there is still the problem of extracting the energy from high energy neutrons without making a Lithium-required blanket radioactive. Whether this amount of Lithium is available and will be effective in containing all the neutrons is doubtful. The investigators in this team based at Foulness decided to cash in on the kudos we had gained to find employment and promotion in fields outside AWRE.

So my experience, which was boosted by having my name on several externally published scientific papers, with hot gases and spectroscopy helped me to gain a position at the Royal Greenwich Observatory at Herstmonceux. After being offered the position, having the audacity to ask what area my work would take and who would be my colleagues and boss before accepting, scuppered any chance of my gaining meteoric promotion. As head of the solar department and researcher in astrophysics my rejection of the Astronomer Royal's offer for me to head up the instrumental division was the final nail in the coffin of any promotion aspirations.

However, in spite of the setbacks, an opportunity to further my education and status presented itself when the Royal Greenwich Observatory formed a link with Sussex University at Brighton. The latter's students were offered observational facilities at the Royal Greenwich Observatory in exchange for members of the Observatory obtaining higher degrees at the University. For the next three years my research at the Observatory on the chemical composition of dwarf stars formed the thesis for my Doctor of Philosophy degree after obtaining an MSc in astronomy by examination and viva voce. The latter proved to be the most nerve racking experience, especially being confronted by the Astronomer Royal, Sir Richard van de Reit Wooley, on the subject of celestial mechanics. My efforts were rewarded with a PhD, the first awarded by Sussex University, in Astrophysics. As with my other degrees my reticence and anti-disestablishment feelings prevented my accepting the award at the degree presentation ceremony. This thread of rejection of authority for its own sake and not conforming to the accepted norm was ever present throughout my life.

To some extent this has limited my advancement in the hierarchies, encountered work wise and socially. This had a beneficial effect of keeping me sane, stress free and happy. Certain problems lead me to volunteer for work at the Radcliffe Observatory in Pretoria, South Africa. Going to South Africa was looked on as going to Siberia astronomically, with the reward of returning with promotion. This was a most enjoyable experience, living in a foreign country rather than just visiting. The Science Research council took over from Naval Scientific Civil Service a few years after my joining the Royal Greenwich Observatory in 1964. At that time the Navy was used to budgeting for battle-ships and the like, costing many millions of pounds sterling. So a new 98″ reflecting telescope to be built in the unsatisfactory site of Herstmonceux in Sussex at a cost of a few millions which was chicken feed to the admirals in Whitehall. Before the telescope was fully commissioned it became apparent, that for observation of faint astronomical objects, the site was a disaster. It had been chosen for its sunshine hours, not for its clear night skies. So the hunt for a new site was initiated.

A friend from my AWRE Foulness days made me aware of a situation with the Atomic Energy Board

(AEB), at Pelindaba on the outskirts of Pretoria, South Africa. The research work involved commissioning of a "Tokamak device", to reproduce the conditions in the sun's centre to burn hydrogen into helium and produce an excess of energy. It was not hard to convince the AEB of my suitability for the position and my subsequent acceptance was forthcoming to return to South Africa. It was a disappointment, that after answering their call to start as soon as possible, to sit around waiting for money to be allocated to the job. Followed by a year waiting for engineering support to get my diagnostics experiments under way. This made me realise that the whole project was a window dressing for something more sinister behind the scenes. Also they reneged on their promise to convert my three year contract into a permanent position at the establishment, shortly after taking up the position. Combining this with the pleas from my children to return to Bexhill and take responsibility for them and their education, which was suffering from a lack of direction, my resignation was tendered. From this point onward my career slowly faded, as the opportunities to work in science research in my mid-forties were rare.

On return to England some eight years were spent in teaching mathematics, physics and computing at various secondary schools in an attempt to find a niche. Finding that education had changed so radically from my days at Wanstead High School, a realisation came to me that my natural abilities did not lie in teaching. After taking various mindless jobs in the real world, my life slipped inevitably into peaceful retirement. Working with non-academic people over this period made me realise that my years spent in research and teaching were in an artificial environment. On reflection my talents would be better utilised in one-off problem solving situations. As I easily get bored of doing the same job, once having grasped the essentials.

Chapter 2

BECOMING A CHRISTIAN

My christening took place in the Anglican Church in Ilford, Essex on November 5 1933.As far as can be detected, the significance of the date, has had no effect on my becoming a Christian. At school there was a Christian assembly every morning, which included a communal recitation of the Lord's Prayer. In the sixth form it was the practice for one of the scholars to read a short passage from the Bible. My turn was not looked forward to with any relish. However, someone did comment that my presentation resembled that of a vicar! However, we still had our children baptized, mainly for the associated social occasion and in order to keep with the trends and fashion current at that time.

Whilst working at the Observatory we finally settled in a house in Hailsham, Sussex next door to a Baptist minister. He had penchant for large fast cars and whilst musing over the size of the engine in his open bonneted car he asked me 'Do you believe in God'. My answer of 'no' was accepted by him and we continued with our conversation over the mechanics of the engine. This seemed to me a very strange reaction from a minister of religion, as my expectation was a lengthy discussion of the reasons for my dis-belief, which would have suited my argumentative nature. My next encounter was aboard 'SA VAAL' bound for South Africa in September 1971, to work on secondment at the Radcliffe Observatory in Pretoria, with my family. We saw a Mr. Rudge having coffee on his own and decided to be sociable and to join him.

We eventually became close friends and he asked me 'If I knew Jesus'. He was not phased by my negative response. Instead he took me to his cabin where he showed me where he was reading about Nicodemus's conversation with Jesus in John chapter 3. Nicodemus was a learned Pharisee who recognised that Jesus was a teacher sent from God as he had performed miraculous signs. Jesus told him that he must be "born again", this time not of flesh but in the Spirit. My position was very similar to that of Nicodemus, in the sense that my arrogance led me to believe that science would have the answers. This was the turning point in my life.

Whilst still on the boat we had further discussions and Mr. Rudge gave me a Bible and passages to read. His patience, generosity and grounding in the Bible made him easy to listen to for long periods. He was on his way to see his brother in Zimbabwe and had on board some Friesian calves for him. On returning to England, in some 3 months time, he promised to send me details of a contact in a church in Pretoria, our final destination. After we disembarked in Cape Town and took delivery of a brand new Volvo 164, we headed for Pretoria via the coastal and picturesque Garden Route.

We arrived in Port Elizabeth and, with my daughter, went for an early morning swim in the sea, the danger signs were on the beach in the form of two tall life-guard platforms. They were empty, however no further thoughts entered my head that we might be in a dangerous situation. After we had been swimming some ten minutes, it came apparent to me that the undertow was slowly taking us out to sea. My daughter responded to my request to swim for the shore and, as she was only nine, made her way back without too much difficulty. My tiredness due to driving for two days previously and the early hour made me weak. My head was being constantly knocked under water with each successive wave and my stomach was filling up from taking in mouthfuls of seawater. My thoughts were that this was the end of my life and was going to die an agonizing death by drowning. Without thinking too long my mind turned unaccountably to Jesus. For the first time in my life my prayer in my mind was 'Please Jesus you have brought me all the way to

South Africa for a new start with my wife. I have a brand new Volvo. Surely it cannot end here.' The next moment my body began to sink, feet first, while still trying to swim weakly to the shore. As this happened my toes just felt the sand in reach and the realization that my feet could stop me from being dragged out to sea by the undertow. The natural cycle of the waves meant that in the period the undertow stopped, my arms and feet could slowly bring me ashore. Stopping the effect of the undertow, on the other part of the cycle each time by just getting enough purchase on the sand with my toes. Eventually inch by inch the shore was reached and made my way slowly back to the hotel. My relief on being saved prompted me to thank Jesus. For the next two days my condition was weak and I was coughing up seawater.

Mr. Rudge was as good as his word and six months later a letter arrived to say that a Mr. Broom was the secretary of the local Brethren church in Pretoria and he would make me welcome at their church. My thoughts had turned away from the drowning incident and the help Jesus had given me in saving my life and centred on my new job. Another six months went by before my thoughts returned to how on two previous occasions death had been very close.

The first occurred in a laboratory in AWRE Foulness. My line manager and myself were under pressure to get some results from an experiment we were conducting. These were needed so that they could be announced at a forthcoming conference. The experiment relied on a bank of low inductance, high voltage (10 kilo volt) lethal condensers to supply a discharge into the shock wave chamber. On one particular occasion the bank did not discharge. With my colleague we investigated why this had not happened. This took place at the end of the day when we were the only two in the building. So we decided, although this was not really our job or expertise in the project, to try and find the fault. Whilst on top of the condenser bank our hands touched and the bank tried to discharge through us! Fortunately our muscles reacted involuntarily by throwing our arms apart and so we received only a bearable shock. We staggered back to our office and plied ourselves with a shot of whisky.

My second narrow escape occurred whilst making winter observations from the observatory some 8000 ft up the Sierra Nevada mountain range in southern Spain. One night the weather suddenly changed and we found ourselves in a snowstorm which was so intense that it was a 'white-out'. With the sleeping arrangements being very primitive in the isolated observatory, we decided to return to the glorious Parador Hotel some half a mile down the mountain. With a compass and torch we, my fellow observer and myself, set out for the Hotel. One of us pointing the torch in the direction of the compass bearing for the hotel, whilst the other walked 25 yards, the limit of the torch beam, in front keeping to the line of the light beam from the torch. Slowly we made our way back. The next day was bright and sunny so we retraced our steps only to find that our footsteps went within two feet of the edge of a 1000 feet precipice on the mountain. How we avoided a disastrous fall was God's providence.

These thoughts in my mind drove me to call on the contact Mr.Rudge had sent me. This was in the road where my first few nights stay in Pretoria were located. Mr.Broom answered the door and told me the details of the Brethren Church in Pretoria, which met every Sunday. Also he told me that it was good that my visit was that day as he was moving the next day. All the apparent coincidences led me to discover more about Christianity. It took a long time before my acceptance of Jesus Christ into my life as my Saviour from sin and as my friend. There was much about the service in the church that countered the aspects of the Church of England service that made me feel uncomfortable and seemed unnecessarily ornate. There was no liturgy, no minister to lead the service and the people were welcoming. Up to this point my only contact with church services were for weddings, christenings and funerals, which prompted me to coin the term 'four wheel Christianity'. My approach to Christianity was similar to that for academic study. My analysis of the gospels did not yield any faults in the spoken words of Jesus. My conclusion was that the gospels could not have been written by a mere human.

At the services my note taking was becoming legendary. The members of the church accepted my questions, which at times were on the point of rudeness, and explained the answers or referred me to the relevant place in the bible. My final acceptance of the truth of Christianity and subsequent step of faith into the unknown came after my return to England in 1973 and finally back to South Africa in 1975. These long journeys between two continents and my near death experiences were all part of God's plan to bring me to the point of realisation of my need and His presence in my life. This certainly turned my life around, gave me a purpose for living and meaning for my existence.

There have been many occasions since in life when my direction and sense of adventure strayed from God's intended path and again had to be rescued. My study of Christianity has been just as interesting and thought provoking, certainly more beneficial and stress free, than any study of science. It represents the 'why' of my life whereas science is the complexity of life, which, in my opinion, will never be fully revealed to us. As does Sir Martin Rees in his book 'Our Cosmic Habitat'. Man is very different from animals and this is not due to some extra ordinary jump in evolutionary process from chimpanzees. Man has a spirit and enquiring mind. He has similar DNA as animals because he was created by the same source.

Chapter 3

RECENT EXPLANATIONS OF
THE STAR OF BETHLEHEM

The Star of Bethlehem is unique in the sense that it is only found in the Book of Matthew of the Bible. Some people would see this as another biblical myth or fairytale embellishment of the unfolding story of Jesus. If this is so, why have there been so many books and scientific papers written on the subject. Nearly every Christmas there appears an article in the paper, a book or television programme discussing what this 'Star' might be. The latest have been the BBC TV 'Star of Bethlehem' on December 24th 2008, Astronomical Enigmas by Mark Kidger in 2005 and The Star of Bethlehem by Patrick Moore in 2005. Each of these will be considered below.

The New International Version of the Bible is a modern and well-researched translation of the Bible from its original available sources in foreign languages, mainly Greek and Hebrew. The reference to the star is in Matthew Chapter 2 verses 1 – 10. *'After Jesus was born in Bethlehem in Judea, during the time of King Herod, Magi from the east came to Jerusalem and asked 'Where is the one who has been born the king of the Jews? We saw his star in the East and have come to worship him.' When King Herod heard this he was disturbed and all Jerusalem with him. When he had called together all the people's chief priests and teachers of the law, he asked them where the Christ was to be born. 'In Bethlehem in Judea' they replied 'for the prophet (Mica) has written 'But you, Bethlehem, in the land of Judah are by no means least among the rulers of Judah; for out of you will come a ruler who will be the shepherd of my people Israel'. Then Herod called the Magi secretly and found out from them the exact time the star appeared. He sent them to Bethlehem and said 'Go and make a careful search for the child. As soon as you find him report to me, so that I too may go and worship him'. After they had heard the King, they went on their way, and the star they had seen in the east went ahead of them until it stopped over the place where the child was. When they saw the child they were overjoyed.'* Also verse 16 in Matthew Chapter 2. *'When Herod realised that he had been outwitted by the Magi (and having been warned in a dream not to go back to Herod) they returned to their country by another route, verse 12a, he was furious, and he gave orders to kill all the boys in Bethlehem and its vicinity who were two years old and under, in accordance with the time he had learned from the Magi.'*

From this extract it can be deduced that the Star of Bethlehem has the following characteristics, which must be met by any explanation of its nature.

The Star was observed first by the Magi when they were in a country east from Jerusalem.

Their journey must have taken the best part of two years as Herod ordered boys of 2 years or under to be killed.

The Star went ahead of the Magi to a place 10km due south from Jerusalem (Bethlehem) until it stopped over the place where Jesus was born. This implies that the star which they were following went ahead of them, stopped over Jerusalem and then, after discussion with Herod, they followed it to Bethlehem.

The location of the Star in the sky was low enough for the Magi to determine the difference between the Star over Bethlehem and Jerusalem, a relatively small distance of 10 km. They were overjoyed to see it still there after their discussions with Herod. It could have reappeared after they had talked to Herod, which could have easily been a few days whilst the chief priests and teachers of the law were gathered together.

Alarmingly, from the point of view of the authenticity of science, no solution for the object can be found in the literature available to me that satisfies all these conditions. The BBC TV programme on The Star of Bethlehem shown on 24th December 2008 was the latest contribution to the subject. This was an hour long programme with contributions from a series of experts from astronomers to historians. The passage read from the bible did not mention the movement of the star from Jerusalem to Bethlehem. The programme first looks at the identity of the Magi. They were seen as Persians who were from the order of priesthood called Magi. In those times there was not a distinction, as there is today, between astrologers and astronomers. They looked for signs among the stars to make their astrological predictions. Among these predictions would be the birth of a king or ruler.

Persia was in modern day Iran and they were expecting a messiah as predicted from the Bible's book of Micah, a Jewish prophet, 'but you Bethlehem Ephrathah though you are small among the clans of Judah, out of you will come forth one who will be ruler over Israel (Micah 5 vs 2) (one of many prophesies about Jesus). The Magi emerge out of the desert, talk to Herod, find the infant Jesus, give their gifts and then hurriedly disappear off in another direction. Without the star they had been following for the best part of two years they could have been lost in the deserts of time. There appears to be no record of them returning to Persia and relating the joyous event. Probably due to the fear of retribution from the long arm of Herod.

The birth of Christ did not take place at 0 BC, as there were some errors made when the calendar was reset in the sixth century to the birth of Christ, which was erroneously given the date of 1 AD. Calculations show from historical records that the birth of Christ was 5 BC. Although some historians favour 6 BC.

Professor Brian Cox, a particle physicist, favours the comet as a contender for the role of Star of Bethlehem. These spend some months passing through the earth's atmosphere making them visible in the night sky whilst this mass of dirty ice and particles are slowly evaporated as the comet comes closer to the sun. Its orbit then takes it away from the sun and it then becomes invisible. This neatly covers the period, some months, when the Magi are on their travels. However, as observed with the recent comet Hale-Bopp in 1997 in England, in the course of the night this was seen to move from the east to the west. In a similar way to the moon in the passage of a night. So there is no way a comet becomes stationery over a place, eg Jerusalem, for months on end so that you could pinpoint a particular place. It behaves like the moon and slowly, during the course of one night, passes from east to west horizons.

The programme makes some play on the fact that a comet appears in early art works and of course on the Bayeaux Tapestry. This comet of 5 BC, of which there is evidence in early observations of the Chinese, could have been the trigger for the Magi looking for other signs. It certainly could not have been the Star of Bethlehem as it does not fit the facts.

45

Professor David Hughes thinks the comet would be seen by the Magi as a harbinger of bad news. There was some discussion whether it was more likely that the Magi, who may have been any number from two to thirty, were not dressed as kings, but as ordinary men and travelled on horseback.

The TV programme then went on to consider the planets as a candidate for the Star of Bethlehem. These were known as 'wandering' stars to early man. As they wandered against the background of stars, they appeared to go round from east to west every 24 hours as did the sun. Presumably these Magi did observe that the planets did not twinkle due to the physical closeness of these objects to the earth. All bright objects in the sky were considered to be 'stars'. David Hughes has investigated the planet Jupiter for over 30 years as an ordinary planet that does extra-ordinary things. He considered the triple conjunction of Jupiter, and Saturn with the constellation of Pisces would be a significant event. As this happens three times over a period of months it would keep the Magi interested in following it. No evidence is presented that the conjunction did not occur at other times before the birth of Jesus. It was suggested that they travelled from Babylon (in now Iran), a distance of 400 – 600 miles depending on the route taken.

Dr Molnar has uncovered a coin minted some time after 0 BC that has the symbol of Aries on one side and a star on the reverse side. The coin comes from the present day Turkey, possibly from Antioch. Aries represented the Jewish nation and the brightest 'star' would be the planet Jupiter. Around the time of the birth of Jesus, Jupiter appeared to go behind the moon as seen from the earth. This is called a lunar occultation, which is a relatively rare event. Dr Molnar's book entitled The Star of Bethlehem published in 1945 looks into the legacy of Magi. The Magi, probably astrologers, believed the new King would be born when the moon passed in front of Jupiter. This is a fascinating book, which deals rather more with the work of the astrologers and the history of the times when they lived. In order to establish the connection between the coin and the reason why the Magi set out on their journey. He is convinced that the Star of Bethlehem did exist and it was not just a myth. He makes no comment on other supernatural events in the Bible such as the creation, parting of the Red Sea, the sun standing still, the virgin birth and the resurrection of Jesus. These are all contained in the Bible and seem to have little chance of being explained by science. Dr. Molnar sees the Magi or astrologers of antiquity, as the scientists of their time. However, he proposes that the extraordinary conditions of the solar planets on April 17, 6BC were as real and as dramatic as any comet or supernova. As this indicates a wonderful message about a regal and divine birth of

Jesus, and not a portent of disaster the other events would signify.

Professor Rick Larson related his view on the Star of Bethlehem being Jupiter. Again there was a proposed error in the calendar and Jesus was born in 2BC. The Magi were stirred up in September 3 BC when Jupiter was in the constellation Regulus. This event occurred three times in several months. So that the Magi would then be setting out on horses or camels with three types of gifts viz. gold, incense and myrrh. In June 2 BC Regulus was in conjunction or meeting with the planet Venus. This planet represents motherhood in ancient writings. On the 25th December 2BC Jupiter stood still against the background of stars, however, the latter were moving in tune with the sun and making their daily apparent encirclement of the Earth.

The Rev. Joanna Jephson pointed out that Kepler, the astronomer who was famous for plotting the orbits of the planets, observed some 400 years ago a triple conjunction of Mars, Jupiter and Saturn. At this time a new star was formed. This was the supernova in the crab nebula in 1604. A supernova is an exploding star that suddenly brightens to many times brighter than the Sun. The Sun has a similar fate, if we are using the correct physics, in some 10,000,000 years. This will mark the end of the earth, as the surface of the Sun will reach the earth as the Sun explodes.

Dr. Mark Kidger considered the 1927 supernova to

be the result of the transfer of mass between two binary stars. In this system of two stars revolving round each other, the larger one deposits matter onto the smaller one. This causes the smaller star to flare up several times. These flares would alert the Magi to some impending spectacular events which will end in a catastrophic supernova explosion at the birth of Christ. The most significant statement in the programme made by a theologian was ' Good scientists would not say we have a solution.' There was no reason given for this statement.

Whilst the programme was very interesting and trawled up some unusual history, it had no favourite candidate for the Star of Bethlehem. One common factor was that they all occurred in the sky around about the time of the birth of Christ, somewhere before 0 BC. However, none of them considered if they were stationary with respect to the earth, how the magi could be directed to Jerusalem and how the particular candidate could move from Jerusalem to Bethlehem.

Secondly the origin of the Star of Bethlehem is discussed in a chapter of Mark Kidger's book entitled Astronomical Enigmas, first published in 2005. At least this work included the Bible's reference to this star and in particular that in verse 9 and 10 'When they had heard the King, they (the Magi) set out from Jerusalem and there, ahead of them, went the star that they had seen rising, until it stopped over the place (Bethlehem) where the child was. When they saw that the star had stopped, they were overwhelmed with joy.' There is then no attempt to accommodate this fact into the likely candidates considered for the Star of Bethlehem. Dr.Kidger recognises that the star must move 10 km south of Jerusalem. Whilst the Magi were in Jerusalem the disappearance of the star would be accounted for by the star being covered up by the moon. It must have been a very short visit to account for the star's disappearance! There is some interesting historical discussion on the date of the birth of Jesus, pointing out errors made in originally relating the calendar by Dionysius Exidious in 525 AD. This concludes that the best estimated date for the birth of Jesus was 5 BC or 6 BC. Mark Kidger believes that the magi were Persian priests of the Zoroastrianism religion. The Gospel of Infancy in the Bible's Apocrypha states that the Magi came to Jerusalem 'according to the prediction of Zoroaster' viz. 'and it came to pass, when the Lord Jesus was born in Bethlehem, a city of Judea in the time of Herod the King, the wise men came from the east to Jerusalem, according to the prophesy of Zoradascht (Zoroaster) and brought with them offerings namely, gold, frankincense and myrrh, and worshipped him and offered to him gifts.' They obviously recognised that this was someone special and had not arrived by chance. In his book Dr. Kidger considers Venus, Uranus, ball lightning, a meteor, the Aurora

Borealis, near-earth asteroid, Halley's Comet, some other comet, a Supernova, an occultation, planetary conjunctions and The Chinese Star.

He finds a reason to dismiss all of these as a potential candidates. He does recognise that ball lightning would fit the bill, however, he has dismissed this as there has been no known ball lightning that has even lasted for a short time and considers it implausible for it to appear and disappear over the long period of his journey. He seems to have lost sight of the notion that the birth of Christ was a very special event that would need an extra ordinary object to signify his birth. Mark Kidger, as in the BBC TV programme, goes with his theory of a series of conjunctions of the planets occurring to heighten the expectations of the Magi. Just as we have no idea when Jesus will return to the earth, the magi had no idea when Jesus would be born. He concludes by stating 'The fact that no single event has yet offered a convincing explanation is perhaps a clue that no one event can explain the star. If there is a simple explanation, though, we are probably as close to it as science can get us.'

Finally Sir Patrick Moore in his book entitled 'The Star of Bethlehem' reviews the situation. The author has relied heavily on the works of Dr. Kidger and Dr. Hughes in making a review of the subject.

He considers the following possibilities:

51

1. The whole story was a myth or invented or promoted by the disciple Saint Matthew.
2. The star was supernatural.
3. The star was a genuine astronomical (i.e. in space) phenomenon.
4. The star was an UFO or flying saucer.

Sir Patrick immediately dismisses the notion that it was a miraculous star or an astronomical object. As this is not in his remit for the book. You would have thought at this point he would have given up on writing the book as the previous works have dealt with the usual candidates. Sir Patrick's requirements for the star, although he has doubts about St Matthew's unique account, are as follows.

Must be unusual.

Conspicuous (at least to the astronomers of the day).

Possibly only seen by the Magi or wise men.

Appeared in the period 7 to 4 BC.

Short lived or had two separate appearances.

Movement unlike any known star or planet.

Sir Patrick maintains that all stars and planets can be dismissed.

Occultation (one astronomical object covering another object), comets, supernova, meteors and conjunctions can be dismissed equally well as they obvious do not fit the criteria. Only a UFO or a flying saucer would fit all the criteria, which Sir Patrick absolutely refuses to believe. His final answer that there is no known astro-nomical object to fit these requirements. Except of course the most obvious one of being a miraculous object to match the miraculous birth of Jesus.

Chapter 4

THE STAR OF BETHLEHEM

After reading the writings on this subject in the previous chapter, it can be seen that this event has stretched the minds of many scientists as to its nature. Only a selection of the latest thoughts and investigations have been mentioned there. A few mention the fact that the star moved some 22 miles from Jerusalem to Bethlehem after the meeting between the Magi and King Herod. Much of the writing discusses what it cannot be and then concentrates on a conjunction between planets and/or constellations of stars. To understand this, the likely nature and profession of the Magi needs to be considered and what would alert them to the great event like the birth of a king. Also the date becomes of some importance and the investigation into the history of the rewinding of the calendar and the history of events around the year 0 BC. Most researchers agree that Jesus was born around 6 BC within a range of a year.

My work in science and astrophysics has been indicated in an earlier chapter and I can only trust that my credentials as a scientist are considered sound. If, maybe, a little cynical, of some of the scientific research attempted on this matter and other academic subjects. Some of these have little bearing on the welfare of mankind but rather on the pure pursuit of knowledge for its own sake. My life as a Christian has resulted in a deep faith in Jesus as revealed in the Bible. Fundamentalism is not a popular label today for someone who believes in a God or many Gods. My Christianity is a practical form based on my helping others through the difficulties of life. It is only as a last resort that my thoughts on the Star of Bethlehem should be put on paper as many other attempts to bring my views to public notice have been thwarted. My aim and delight would be that people will no longer trot out their pet theory every Christmas or Epiphany on the subject. Instead they will accept that it was a unique event consistent with the importance of the birth of Jesus. Not just another occultation, nova, comet, supernova or other well charted event.

We should accept that Jesus was born at the most opportune moment in the history of mankind. That everything He said and that was written about Him has great significance for today. So this event which was labelled a star in Matthew's account cannot be called a star in the true sense of the meaning of the word now. To understand the nature of this object in the sky we must put ourselves in the mind of the Magi. One day they woke up to find that there was a new light in the western sky. This is the sign they expected for the birth of a king. This was so unusual and spectacular that they decided to follow it, apparently on camels or horseback, taking with them provisions for a long journey and presents for the new king.

This light was not an astronomical object out in space, which would have disappeared over the horizon and reappeared behind them in the course of the day. It was unlikely that they took to the sea as Dr.Kidger contemplated in his book 'Astronomical Enigmas', as this would have meant that they knew where they were going. Any star, planet, supernova, comet or other astronomical object out in space would appear to move closely with the stars due to the earth rotating on its axis. Today we are used to the idea of a stationary artificial satellite that has a constant position in the sky relative to our stationary position on earth. We are able to receive SKY television and mobile phone transmissions because they rely on fixed (relative to us) satellites. So far only a plane, similar to the Concorde in speed, would be able to keep up with movement of stars, planets and comets. Although an artificial satellite could be seen over the journey of some 400 – 600 miles, the distance the Magi would have to travel if they came from Persia (now known as Iran), it would need to be 10 km high in the sky, some 6 miles, for the magi to get an accurate fix of the place of the birth of Jesus to within 22 miles. This would be necessary to distinguish Bethlehem from Jerusalem. It could be done without sophisticated instruments if the Magi looked down at the reflection of the star in a very deep well. There is no indication that there were many wells in this area of the country, let alone deep enough to determine if the object was directly overhead. Also another condition would be that the 'star' was bright enough to follow by day or by night, but not too bright to attract the attention of people as they went about their daily tasks. In the late 1970's Venus was close enough to be seen by day if you knew where to look for it. My own awareness came to me lying on my back in a swimming pool in Pretoria, South Africa. At first my gaze at the bright sky could not locate it in spite of my friend pointing it out to me. Once it was caught in my vision it was incredibly easy to locate again after averting my gaze. It must have been the same for the Magi. Once they had seen it at night then they could then see it by day, as they knew where to look.

The birth of Christ and his subsequent resurrection after death were miraculous events. These have stood the test of time for 2000 years. There have been many intelligent people who have tried to prove that these did not happen, all of whom have failed. Some have been converted to the truth of Christianity in their attempts to find a plausible alternative answer. The author, Frank Morrison, of 'Who moved the Stone' was one such person. We have other miraculous events in the Bible besides the creation of the world, the parting of the Red Sea and Noah's flood. When Moses was fleeing from Egypt they followed a pillar of cloud by day (probably like a tornado) and by night a pillar of fire. Although the latter does not seem to have an equivalent phenomenon that is known today, it would not have been mistaken as a star.

Surendra Verma in his book entitled 'The Tunguka Fireball' (subtitled Solving One of the Greatest Mysteries of the 20th Century) describes how at 7.14 am (Russian time) on June 30th 1908 a huge fireball exploded over Siberia. It flattened an area the size of greater London with a force a thousand times the force of Hiroshima, creating a mushroom cloud that almost reached in space. For over 100 years scientists have tried to solve the mystery of this event. The title of the book is not borne out in the text, as the book's conclusion is that nobody knows for sure! Like the extinction of the dinosaurs by Noah's flood, it certainly occurred, but the actual mechanism is unknown.

Writing of this booklet has been cathartic for me. Every year presents itself, at Christmas, with my frustration and incredulity that once again in books, the papers, TV and other media outlets, this old chestnut that the 'star' of Bethlehem was an astronomical object. There are two main categories of scientific research in Physics and maybe other disciplines. One uses discoveries made to improve the life of the human race and, increasingly, animals. Others like astronomers, evolutionists and others try to find a theory for their observations. The second types spend huge amounts of money, time and mental effort trying to fit a theory to match the known facts. This usually requires more knowledge and observations which, as often as not, needs the theory to be changed. Classic examples of this are the theory of the nature of quasars, the big bang theory, theory of evolution and the structure of the atom. There are such fundamentals, why masses attract and why like-charges of electricity repel, that no one is presently near discovering. The treatment of the subject of the nature of the Star of Bethlehem is typical of one type of approach to research, viz. the bending of the facts of the case to fit the theory. Darwin was a careful and methodical scientist who waited until he was reasonably certain of his results before publishing.

However, there are many gaps in the evidence that out of the 'big bang' or primeval explosion of hydrogen atoms (the simplest form of matter) so densely packed that the whole universe was the size of a pinhead, with unimaginably large amounts of energy, came mankind. There is no mechanism to explain how mankind changed from atoms, to amoeba, to fish, to animals, to primates, to us. The only mechanism proposed for this chain of events is a seemingly reasonable hypothesis that there will be the survival of the fittest. Many evolutionists, including Richard Dawkins and David Attenborough, defend these philosophies of life by calling into question the sanity and mental capacity of Christians. This shows to me how bare their arguments are when they have to resort to such tactics. Nothing has been proved or ever will be, as it is in the realms of unrecorded history and does nothing to disprove creation. Already the survival of the fittest theory has been abandoned as a reason for these changes. Many of the great scientists like Einstein, and of our time Stephen Hawking do not believe all this happened by chance. Most of the ugliness of this world has been produced by man's intervention. However, could we possibly end up with such a beautiful and diverse natural world just by chance. Surely nature is crying out with a loud voice there is a creator. A more comprehensive, extremely well researched, and well written account of 'Has science disproved God' is contained in Nicky Gumbel's book entitled 'Is God a Delusion.'

From the above discussion and references it can be seen that the Star of Bethlehem cannot be explained by any known physical object. This unique event can be explained by considering that the Star of Bethlehem could have been a fireball 10,000 metres up in the sky (i.e. about the height of Everest) which went ahead of them. A fireball consists of a plasma of high energy protons and electrons contained by a strong magnetic field, produced by the high speed rotation of these charged particles. Man has attempted to produce these in laboratory conditions with some limited success. It is difficult to hold the plasma together for more than a short amount of time. The fireball stopped over Jerusalem where the magi made their inquiries and spoke to Herod. It then reappeared when they left Jerusalem and went ahead of them to Bethlehem. This then fits all the conditions of the 'star' detailed in Matthew Chapter 2. Only those so smitten with the idea that science has the answer to everything in the universe would not be able to accept this explanation.

EPILOGUE

There is now among evangelical Christians a move afoot, on an individual basis, to 'cherry pick' the Bible. Science has become the new saviour of the people and is seen as the answer to all our problems. Releasing us from the drudgery of life and curing all our diseases. In the latter, cloning may turn out to be a step too far. Also some medical conditions have been identified and are now much more prevalent. For example psychologically related allergies, mutations, depression and MRSA illnesses. Mankind is becoming more prone to the diseases that were unheard of a century ago. In some ways it was much easier living in the days of Jesus.

The 'cherry picking' started with creation and people accepting the conclusion of science that the world started with evolution from the Big Bang or an explosion from a point flinging matter in all directions. Even if one could conceive the tremendous amount of energy present in a point for the 'big bang' to occur, we then have to accept that we have arrived at this present point in time by random processes and mutation, to a world, different, but with well defined, species of animal life and flora. On top of this mind stretch, this development has produced a beautiful natural kaleidoscope around us that has not been surpassed by those of man's construction. Albeit they show his ingenuity and skill. Now we have Christians who would dismiss the flood at the time of Noah. Also other parts of the Old Testament, such as the walls of Jericho tumbling down. These occurrences are labelled by some as myths, created by early simpleminded people looking for an explanation for the world in which they lived. The dominance of the feminist movement in recent times has sought the abandoning of the writings of St Paul and St Peter that are contrary to man and woman being equal in social and intellectual standing. They discuss sections of the Bible as part of the culture prevalent at the time of Jesus.

Among the more academic Christian fraternity the virgin birth and the physical resurrection have been questioned. These are the 'rock' of the Christian faith, and reduces Jesus to, at best, a prophet. Some would write him down as an opportunist madman.

The writing of this booklet has strengthened my faith and my determination to hold fast on the truth of the whole bible and accept the total package. The star of Bethlehem being just one of many events which need a miraculous explanation. Science can do many things, but will never find an explanation of all the miraculous events described in the Bible. There is one aspect that is very hard to express or describe in words, this is the reality of the presence of God in my life. My life has taken some bad turns, mainly of my own making. However, this has not been by chance. My one to one relationship with God through Jesus grows daily as my trust in Him grows. Hiccups along the way have been many, but every day my thoughts and actions become closer to that of our Maker. If just one person's mindset has been changed by reading this account, then my efforts to come to grips with modern printing techniques will have been worthwhile. Sir Martin Rees in his book 'Our Cosmic Habitat' states some ultimate questions 'lie beyond science.' When mixing and working with the famous my attitude has always been one of an open joker with a quiet and serious side. My latest T shirt carries the relevant esoteric strap line 'There positively is a God now stop worrying and enjoy life.' My best friend from college days, cannot understand my Christian belief and has used every scientific argument to dissuade me from my faith. This has made me see how weak he and the scientific community arguments are in trying to support atheism. Each day my conversation with Jesus brings me closer to Him and His teachings help me in the battle with the Devil. Science has shown me how complex and intricate the world is in which we live. There is no proof, or ever will be, on how this universe came into being – only speculation. There is written proof of the existence of Jesus, his birth being foretold in the history of the Jews (the Old Testament of the Bible) and the experience of many Christians and non-Christians of the Holy Spirit of God over a period of 2000 years.

Professor Dawkins can be as insulting as he likes about Christians and their belief in Jesus, but this only shows the weakness of the theory of evolution when he has to resort to these tactics. Being in a minority does not make my thinking wrong. Being part of the crowd baying for the crucifixion of Jesus is being rerun in our time by those who think mankind will have all the answers, and Jesus was just a prophet or something worse.

There is hope for all peoples, including many scientists, to lose the shackles of this world and enter a new one. This asks for a step of faith into the unknown and to have complete faith in a god who is found in every word of the Holy Bible. Seek and you will find. Turn your back and the devil will be happy to keep you for his own. You will enter a different dimension, not one of the ten (or is it eleven now?) that Stephen Hawking needs to describe his universe. In his latest book entitled "The Grand Design", Stephen and his co-author talks about model dependent realism and multiple universes. When he talks about the existence of every possible history you know he has possibly tied himself in knots with the string theory! Perhaps he is pulling our collective legs (which come of the trousers found in his book "A brief history of time").

Charles Darwin blamed God for the death of his daughter and lost faith in Him. My son, in spite of his devotion to work and pleasure, will be there to greet me because he had made the decision to give his life to Jesus and we will have a good laugh about our time together.

The world's problems will not be solved by more laws and throwing excessive amounts of money into the cause. This has been clearly shown in the history of the Jewish nation, delightfully and carefully recorded in the Old Testament. The solution is for everyone to follow Jesus and bring heaven to earth. AMEN.

GLOSSARY OF TERMS

Ball Lightening. An atmospheric electrical phenomenon with spherical diameter in the order of 0.05 metres to several metres, which lasts for many seconds. Probably a hot gas or plasma of charged atoms of nitrogen and oxygen. So far due to rarity and unpredictability of unknown nature.

Big Bang. A term coined by Sir Fred Hoyle in 1950's for the start of the universe with a hot massive explosive event of small physical size about 10 billion years ago.

Comet. This is an icy body of material that releases gas and dust when warmed by the Sun on its approach. It is observed by the reflected light from its tail when it comes close to the Sun. The comet has an elongated orbit and most of its path is distant from the Sun.

Conjunction. When two planets or astronomical objects appear in the same straight line when seen by an observer on earth or other point in space.

Constellation. A group of stars or other visible astronomical objects within a particular region of the sky. The sky is divided in 88 areas or constellations. The stars in any constellation are not necessarily at the same distance.

Cosmos. The space in which we live. Alternatively called the known universe.

DNA. The chemical shorthand name for deoxyribonucleic acid, which is a thin chain of like molecules. These are found in every living cell and directs the formation, reproduction and growth of cells.

Googling. A term meaning using a computer programme (found on the website www.google.co.uk) to search a comprehensive number of articles that contain the reference to the word or phrase under investigation. This is one of many search engines.

Hiroshima. The town in Japan hit by the first atomic bomb in June 1945.

Lithium. An element with atomic number three, having the ability to absorb fast neutrons.

Messiah. In the Jewish religion he is the King of Israel from the House of David. Christians believe this to be Jesus.

Neutron. This is a sub-atomic particle without charge with a mass slightly larger than a proton. Found as a building block of the atomic nuclei.

Occultation. In astronomy this is the covering of one astronomical object by another in the line of sight. An eclipse is one form of occultation.

Planet. This is a large inert mass that orbits a much larger luminous mass. They are usually seen by reflected light.

Proton. Is a positively charged sub-atomic particle.

Solar System. Consists of a number of planets and smaller masses orbiting the earth.

Venus. This is the second closest planet to the sun with a mass a little less than that of the earth, and part of the solar system.

Uranus. The seventh most distant planet from the sun, with at least five satellites or moons. It is nearly fifteen times heavier than the earth.

REFERENCES

Alexander Denis 'Creation or Evolution – Do we have to choose' Monarch Books, Oxford (2008).

Allison. D.C. 'What was the Star That Guided the Magi?' Bible Review 9, No 6: p.20-24, 63 (1993).

Burke's Peerage, Baronetage and Knightage, Ed. Charles Mosley, 107th Edition, Wilmington Press, Delaware, USA (2003).

Bulmer, Thomas, Ivor 'The Star of Bethlehem – A new explanation – Stationary Point of a Planet', Q.J.R.A.S., 33 (1992)

Barke, Gaffnet W. 'Kepler and the Star of Bethlehem', Journal RAS, Canada, 417-25, (1937).

Chapman, Rietsehi P.A.L. 'Venus as the Star of Bethlehem' Q.J.R.A.S., 37, p.843 (1996).

Clark, David M., John H. Parkinson and Richard F. Stevenson 'An Astronomical Re-appraisal of the Star of Bethlehem – A Nova in 5 BC' Q.J.R.A.S., 18, p.443-49, (1997).

Dawkins, Richard, 'The God Delusion' London Bantam, (2006).

Freitag, Ruth S. 'The Star of Bethlehem' A list of References, Library of Congress, Washington D.C. (1979).

Hawking, Stephen W. and Mlodinow, Leonard, London, Transworld Publishers (2010).

Hughes, David, 'The Star of Bethlehem: An Astronomers Confirmation', New York, Walker and Co (1979).

Hughes, David, 'The Star of Bethlehem Mystery', London, J.M. Dent and Sons Ltd. (1979).

Humphreys, Colin J. 'The Star of Bethlehem – A comet in 5 B.C. – and the Date of the Birth of Christ'. Q.J.R.A.S. 32, p. 389 – 407 (1991).

Gumbel, Nicky, 'Is God a Delusion', Holy Trinity Brompton, London, (2008).

Jackel, Ted. 'The God Particle' Universal Publishers, U.S.A. (2007)

Kidger, Mark 'Astronomical Enigmas', John Hopkins, University Press, p. 49 –71 (2005).

Molaar, Michael. R. 'The Star of Bethlehem – The Legacy of the Magi' Rutgers University Press. (1945).

Moore, Patrick. 'The Star of Bethlehem' Canopus Press Ltd, London , (2001).

Morison, Frank. 'Who moved the Stone'. Authentic Media, Milton Keynes, UK. (2006).

Mosley, John. 'The Christmas Star'. Los Angeles, Griffin Obs. (1987).

Rees, Martin. 'Our Cosmic Habitat'. London: Weidenfield & Nicolson. (2001)

Sumot, Roger. W. 'Thoughts on the Star of Bethlehem'. Sky and Telescope 36, No. 6, p.384-86 (1968)

Tipler, F. J. 'The Star of Bethlehem'. Observatory Vol. 125, p.107. (2005)

Verma, Surendra. 'The Tunguska Fireball', Icon Books (2005).